May all your
christmas dreams
come true !
With love,

Marilee Jos Masfield

The Snowman's Song

A Christmas Story

illustrations by Tracy La Rue Hohn

story by Marilee Joy Mayfield

Leaping Antelope Productions® books are available for sales promotions, premiums and fund-raising use. Special editions can also be created to specification. For details, contact the publishers at Leaping Antelope Productions® 1-888-909-LEAP, www.leapingantelope.com.

Illustrations by Tracy La Rue Hohn
www.larueoriginals.com

Publisher's Cataloging-In-Publication Data
(Prepared by The Donohue Group, Inc.)

Mayfield, Marilee Joy.
   The snowman's song : a Christmas story / illustrations by Tracy La
Rue Hohn ; story by Marilee Joy Mayfield.

     p. : ill. ; cm.
   A forlorn little snowman yearns for a melodic voice so that he can
rejoice by singing Christmas carols.
   ISBN-13: 978-0-9762059-1-3
   ISBN-10: 0-9762059-1-2

1. Christmas stories, American--Juvenile fiction. 2. Snowmen--Juvenile
fiction. 3. Caroling--Juvenile fiction. 4. Christmas stories. 5.
Snowmen--Fiction. 6. Carols--Fiction. I. Hohn, Tracy La Rue. II.
Title.

PS3563.A94 S66 2006
813.6   2005933388

*There is not enough darkness in the world
to extinguish the light
of one small candle.*

Spanish proverb

The Snowman's Song

A Christmas Story

It's true, you know,
that people of snow
send their thoughts around
without making a sound.

Their feelings become
small jewels of pure ice
and they sense these frost drops
like a snowy cold spice.

"*I want to sing!*"
The little snowman
sent this thought to his mother.

"*I want to go 'a caroling'*
like a happy child with a silvery voice.
It's Christmastime, I want to rejoice!"

"*Snow people can't sing,*"
his mother thought sadly.

"*We're made of snow and it makes no sound.*
A child of snow doesn't have a voice.
I'm sorry, my son, you don't have a choice."

But her little son snowman
had so many strong wishes
he wanted to share
that he made a windstorm
of whirling thought air.

"I want my voice to be like church bells
or like harps that angels play in the clouds!
I want my voice to be bright, happy and loud
so all the people and creatures of earth
will hear my proud hymn to our Savior's birth."

A tiny bright bird with a darting quick pace
wrapped her feet on his tree arm and sang near his face.
Her thoughts formed soft snow notes so sweet and clear,
he almost felt he had ears to hear.

"Why can't *I* sing like you?"
thought the little snowman.

"*Of* course, you can."
She sent this thought back to him
as she touched his snow head with the tip of her wing.

"But first you really need to believe
that no matter what anyone thinks back to you,
it just isn't true
that a snowman can't sing."

"How can I do that?
Everyone tells me I don't have a choice.
I'll never make music or have my own voice."

"I'm not sure how you do it,"
she sent back her warm thoughts.

"I just know before you can change who you are
you have to believe.
Feel it deep in your heart.
Think strong thoughts in your mind.
Even when there's no hope, you must see a star."

So the sad little snowman put on a brave face.
He worked hard to replace
his doubts and his fears
with thoughts of sweet songs,
music, bells ringing, and choirs.

Deep in his heart like a candlelit fire
his bright wish remained, his one heart's desire.

The sun always cheered him, at dawn he felt strong.
He tried to have hope that his voice would soon flower.
Would this be the day? Would this be the hour?
But his spirit grew weak as the day became long.

Each day was a chance to make a new start,
but by night he cried ice and felt sad in his heart.

Sometimes he looked up
for signs in the sky.
But nothing was happening.
He couldn't make sounds.

Despite all his wishing, no one seemed aware
that deep in the park, in the snow, he was there.

But one day he woke up and something was new.
The morning was crisp, the sky was bright blue.

He felt powdery footsteps…
"Mommy, look what I found!"
A small girl stood near him, then she jumped up and down.
Her eyes were so happy, her thoughts like bright light.
Her warm voice was filled with pure Christmas delight.

"He's such a cute snowman!
Could I stay and play for a while?"

"Of course, you can, dear. I'll be right here.
Just have a good time."

For most of the day, she played beside him.
She straightened his hat and turned up its brim.
She draped her red winter scarf around his round middle.
She sang him three songs and she told him a riddle.
Then she dangled her store-bought glass beads and charms
all over his long carrot nose and both arms.

"Do you think he can hear me?"
she asked her mother.

"Are you crazy?" sneered her big brother.
He rolled his eyes.
"Who told you those lies?
Snowmen can't hear anything that you say."

"Let's go home," said her mom.
We'll come back another day."

But the little girl didn't want to go home.
Her once joyful thoughts took a more somber tone.
She ran up to the side of his sad snowy face
and whispered these words, which felt like an embrace.

"I know you can hear me.
I really believe it.
I think you are special,
I'll never forget
the day that we spent.
I hear your music even though you can't speak."

And then she leaned over and kissed his cold cheek.

He wanted so much to sing just one small note.
But nothing would come from his cold, hard snow throat.
If only she knew he could hear in his head
the sweet gentle grace of the words she had said.

But something was happening…
he just didn't know
for where she had kissed him
she left a warm glow.
And little by little the snow melted spaces
leaving tiny pearl strings of small open places
from the side of his face to the base of his throat
like the holes in a flute that play very high notes.

The night before Christmas
was the worst night he'd had.
All around there was music.
Everyone seemed so glad.

He silently stood in his place in the park.
His feelings were frozen, his thoughts were so dark.
His mother was worried, she felt his despair
and she tried to send comfort to him through the air.

He knew that she cared.
But his cold heavy silence was too sad to be shared.
The loss of his dreams was too much to shoulder
and they wouldn't come back even if he had told her.

He bowed his head and shut his eyes tight.
Snow was starting to fall, it was such a cold night.
With the last ounce of courage that only faith brings
his thoughts formed this prayer with frost-covered wings.

"Please let me sing a song filled with light.
Then my life will be perfect, my thoughts will be right.
And all the sweet sounds angels use to stop doubt
will burst forth from my heart and out of my mouth
like a powdery snow over this holy night."

He almost missed her soft steps in the snow.
She was holding a candle that gave a warm glow.
It was the small girl, she had brought him a gift.
She sensed all his tears, his soul needed a lift.

'Round his neck there was tinkling, like spoons hitting glass.
She had made him a necklace in her second grade class.
Silver bells, gold stars, and snowflakes of blue,
it was beautifully fashioned and it made music, too.

This gesture of kindness made his heart feel so light.
His spirit was lifted, he forgot all his sorrow.
No more thoughts of tomorrow.
No more thoughts of the past.
He just loved this one moment.
He wanted to freeze it,
just so it would last.

Then the winter wind came
with a huge, forceful blast.
The tinkling bell necklace swirled 'round very fast.
And all of a sudden the holes near his face
blew out lyrical sounds like a heavenly flute.
The whole world stood in place.
His dream was fulfilled, he was no longer mute.

His song was spring rains and violin strings,
the fragrance of flowers and hummingbird wings,
words of great kindness, the faith in our hymns,
the shine in our eyes and a little girl's whims.
More joyful than angels, more peaceful than sleep,
filled with longing and prayers and memories to keep.

All the love in his mind, all the light in his soul,
his dreams for the future, his hopes to be whole
were the notes of his music, his own unique psalm.
Her soft, giving spirit had made his thoughts calm.

She knew he had heard her.
It was golden and true.
The wonder of Christmas
surrounded these two.

For this sweet frozen moment,
this small speck of time,
in heaven and earth
everything was sublime.

TRACY LA RUE HOHN

A native of the San Francisco Bay Area, Tracy graduated from San Jose State University with a degree in Graphic Design/Illustration. Directly after graduating, she entered the graphic design field. In 1988 she began pursuing her freelance career with a specialization in Children's Illustration. Since then she has worked on more than 15 books as well as a number of other artistic projects, including others with Leaping Antelope Productions.

Experienced in all kinds of media, Tracy has found that watercolor is her true love, but in keeping with the times, she has learned to use various graphic programs that help her achieve the same look and feel as her traditional work.

Her favorite subjects are whimsical animals and playful children, and she hopes that the joy she receives from creating these characters carries through to her viewers.

Tracy's website is www.larueoriginals.com.

MARILEE JOY MAYFIELD

Marilee has been involved in writing, teaching and publishing since she first wrote a series of magazines with her sister, when she was eleven years old and her sister was eight.

She started her career as a teacher, but she found she loved writing and editing educational books for children and young adults just as much as teaching, so she tried to find a way to do both. For ten years she worked in educational publishing, first as an assistant editor for middle school textbooks, then as an associate editor for high school textbooks and later as a developmental editor for college textbooks. Her interest in developmental editing and marketing eventually led to a position as a product manager.

Today Marilee lives with her husband in Palo Alto, California. They own two companies together and can kiss each other in the middle of the workday whenever they want.

Marilee loves to hear from her readers. She can be reached at mjmayfield@leapingantelope.com.

Other books by Marilee Joy Mayfield

The Golden Cricket: A Story of Luck and Prosperity
with Illustrations by Randy Jennings

Crabby Lessons
with Illustrations by Randy Jennings

The Tiny Adventures of Big Sister and Little Sister
with Illustrations by Crista Kathleen McGinley

Big Sister, Little Sister
with Illustrations by Crista Kathleen McGinley

Sweet Sister Memories
with Illustrations by Crista Kathleen McGinley

For more information about our wonderful books and posters for children
(and young-hearted grown-ups)
please visit us at www.leapingantelope.com.